My Son's Battle with Cancer

A Story of Survival and Triumph over Neuroblastoma

Noor Mohamad Aman

Praise

"My Son's Battle with Cancer: A Story of Survival and Triumph over Neuroblastoma" by Noor Mohamad Aman vividly captures the author's harrowing journey as he confront his son's agonizing battle with cancer, a profoundly distressing illness that inflicts a relentless wave of sadness and sorrow upon any parent. Yet, through the unwavering dedication and patience of Noor, the father, along with his unshakeable faith in the Almighty, he faced this seemingly insurmountable challenge with remarkable resilience, serving as an enduring source of inspiration for his family. Noor's relentless determination and his heartfelt supplications, offered ceaselessly, day and night, became the conduit for a miraculous recovery, effectively guiding his son towards a path of healing. This poignant account serves as a poignant lesson for those who might find themselves confronted with similar circumstances, urging them not to relinquish hope or succumb to despair. May Allah grant continued health and well-being to the cherished son."

DR ALI MOHAMED SALAH, Director of Iqra Foundation, and Imam of Tawfiiq Islamic Center, Oslo, Norway.

"Receiving a cancer diagnosis is challenging and for children in particular, it can be hard to accept. This book is a source of inspiration and hope that cancer can be treated. In addition, the book raises the level of awareness about childhood malignancies. The case of Hamid's battle with cancer vividly depicts the significance of family psychosocial support."

DR ABDULLAHI ABDI, Senior Medical officer, and Founder and CEO FamilyFirst medical centre, Garissa, Kenya.

"Every child with cancer deserves to be treated and be cured of their disease. Hamid was diagnosed with a cancer that is almost incurable in low and middle income countries. He was treated in a high income country, Norway, and now, three years after his therapy, we can celebrate his progress. My greatest joy would be to have more children in our settings have access to most of the lifesaving care just like Hamid. This is because all children deserve to have a chance to live to their greatest potential."

DR. DOREEN KARIMI, Paediatric Haematologist Oncologist, Gertrude's Children's Hospital, Nairobi, Kenya.

My Son's Battle with Cancer

A Story of Survival and Triumph over Neuroblastoma

Noor Mohamad Aman

First Published 2023

ISBN: 978-82-303-6056-9

Connect with the author
on email: cancer.neuroblastoma @gmail.com

Cover Art by Noor Aman
Cover design by Noor Aman

OSLO, NORWAY

Contents

Dedication

I would like to dedicate this book to my lovely son, Hamid and other children, anywhere they are, who have suffered or are suffering the dire effects of Neuroblastoma.

My dear son, ever since you were born, you have been a major source of joy and fulfilment in my life and the whole family. And ever since your experience with Neuroblastoma, you have been my motivation; you inspire me more than you can imagine. Your strength and resilience in the midst of the cruellest disease has been awe-inspiring.

Hamid, you were patient and strong even as this disease ravaged through your body and weakened you in ways even I will never truly understand. Seeing just how strong you were through it all makes me confident that you will make a big contribution to society and the world in the future.

I cannot wait to see what the future holds for you. I'm looking forward to you having a fulfilling life in which you achieve all your dreams, get married, and have children of your own. I have no doubt that you will be successful in everything you put your mind to.

Hamid, I hide my tears every time I think about you. You are a walking miracle and a source of pride and joy to not only me, but also to our whole family.

My love for you shall abound forever.

Author's note

This book is based on true, personal experiences and accounts of the journey around of my son's battle with, survival and triumph over, Neuroblastoma cancer. The purpose of this book is to share our family's story around the subject and the experiences, provide inspiration to others who may be in similar situations, and raise awareness about childhood cancer and its impact on affected individuals and their loved ones.

Most importantly, it aims to show that every individual's experience with cancer is unique, and the medical information, treatment protocols, and outcomes described in this book are specific to my son Hamid's case. Therefore, the content of this book is not meant to be considered medical advice or a substitute for professional medical consultation, diagnosis, or treatment.

Readers are urged to consult with qualified healthcare professionals, medical experts, and specialists to seek accurate and up-to-date information about Neuroblastoma, its symptoms, treatments, and potential side effects. Each person's medical journey is influenced by various factors, including but not limited to age, overall health, stage of cancer, and individual response to treatment.

The emotional and psychological impact of battling cancer, both on the patient, their family and friends, can be profound and multifaceted. The experiences and emotions shared in this book are reflective of our personal journey and may not align with the experiences of others in similar situations.

It is crucial to recognize that medical research and treatment options for cancer are continually evolving. Therefore, some information presented in this book may become outdated over time. We encourage readers to stay informed and refer to reputable sources for the latest developments in cancer research and treatment.

We extend our heartfelt appreciation to all the healthcare professionals, caregivers, friends, and family who supported us throughout Hamid's battle with Neuroblastoma. Their dedication and love have been invaluable, and this book serves as a tribute to their unwavering support.

We hope that by sharing our story, this book will offer solace, encouragement, and insights to those navigating their own journey through cancer or supporting someone with cancer. Our ultimate aspiration is to raise awareness about Neuroblastoma and childhood cancer, fostering empathy and understanding in our community.

Thank you for joining us in this personal journey and for your compassion in reading "My sons battle with cancer".

Chapter 1: Joy Short-lived

"Bad news is an opportunity for us to rise above ourselves and be more than we think we can be." — Josephine Angelini

1

January 19, 2017.

What an unforgettable day that was! I remember it literally like it was just yesterday.

My whole life was about to change.

It was the day that my beloved wife, Fardowsa, and I welcomed a delightful and healthy bouncing 2.8 kg baby boy into the world, and boy I tell you, I could not have been more thrilled.

-Hamid.

Our first-born child. Born in Garissa Nursing Home Hospital. A wonderful ray of joy and sunshine had just come into our lives.

I was over the moon.

He made his grand entry into this world almost one year after the day Fardowsa and I got married in March 2016 in Garissa, as if he had consciously decided to give us exactly one year to be alone together as a newlywed couple.

I am rarely speechless but this time around, I was lost for words. It was as if the months of anticipation, nerves, and anxiety had balled up in my throat and stolen my words.

No words could adequately capture just how happy I was to be a father. But what my words could not utter, my heart and eyes could not contain. My heart swelled with pride and excitement, and the silent tears of joy would not stop flowing.

I was a dad!

My mini-me was finally here, in the flesh. A reality. A living, breathing being that had my blood and DNA coursing through his veins.

I had dreamt of this moment for such a long time, so the fact that it had finally come to pass was completely surreal and dreamlike.

It is every man's dream to be a father, and I was certainly no exception. The thought of raising a child and watching them grow up to be healthy, happy, and productive members of society is something that I had really looked forward to and now, it had become a reality and everything had gone well with the pregnancy.

The coming days were all perfect and I could not ask for more as a first-time dad. Hamid was healthy, and though he didn't pass urine until 3 days after birth, he was in great health. my wife was healthy too and all the pre-pregnancy check-ups were fine.

As per our customs, he was circumcised 3 days after birth on January 22nd 2017 and two days later, on the 24th, we carried out the traditional goat slaughtering custom where two goats were slaughtered.

A few months later, in June, we got him his Norwegian passport from the Norwegian Embassy in Nairobi.

Over the next 18 months, he was fully vaccinated and his growth chart was perfectly normal— he was 5.7kg at 2 months, 6.6kg at 3 months, 7kg at 7 months and 10kg at 9 months. Hamid's Growth Chart is given in Figure 1 while Hamid's Immunization Card is given in Figure 2.

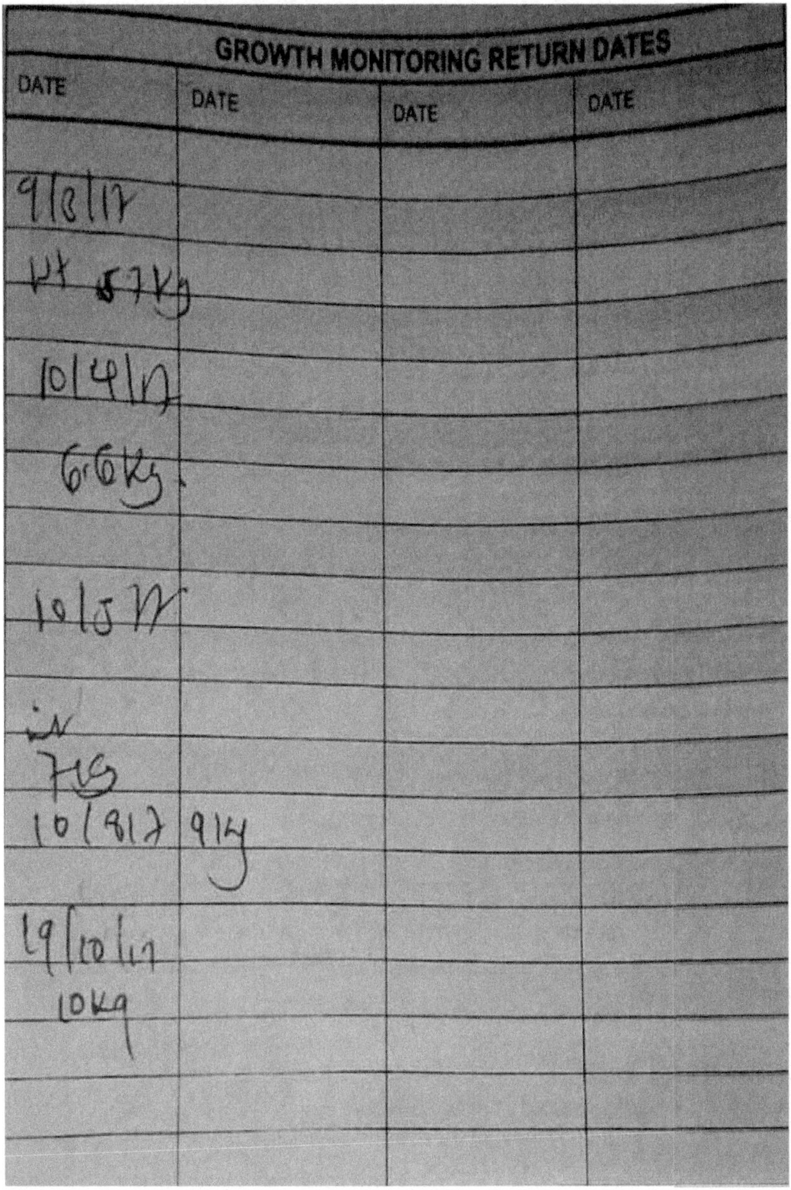

GROWTH MONITORING RETURN DATES			
DATE	DATE	DATE	DATE
9	8	17			
wt 87kg			
10	4	17			
6·6kg			
10	5	17			
wt 7kg			
10	9	17	9	4		
19	10	17			
10kg			

Figure 1: Hamid's Growth Chart.

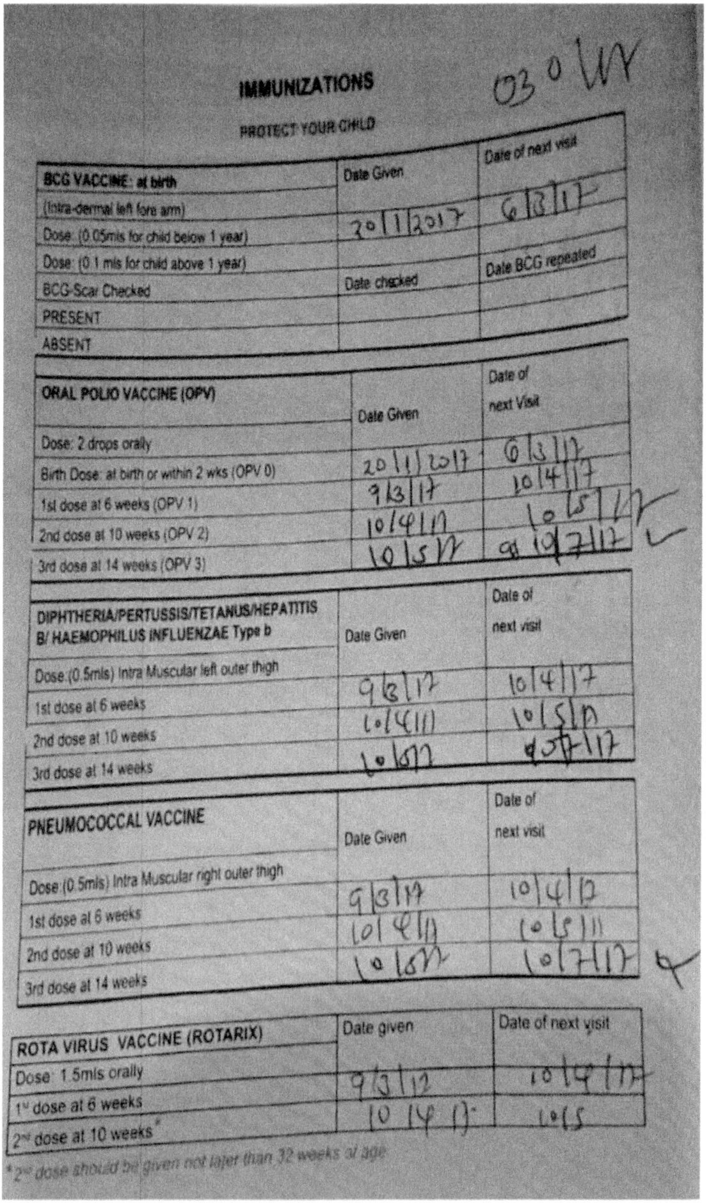

Figure 2: Hamid's Immunization Card.

Hamid hit every developmental milestone like any other healthy infant and we took care of him the best way we knew to make sure that he was well nurtured and strong.

Everything looked perfectly normal. Hamid was doing great!

And I looked forward to being a new father. I looked forward to celebrating all his firsts. His first word. His first step. His first taste of real food other than his mother's milk.

Everything!

I knew that being a father would not be a walk in the park but I did not mind. Nothing good comes easy, after all.

I was up for the challenge!

Or so I thought.

****

It was March 28, 2019.

23 days after the birth of our second son, Ammaar.

11 days after I had arrived back in Norway from Garissa.

At the time, I was working full-time in Norway, while Fardowsa and my two young sons lived in Garissa so I used to travel back and forth between Garissa and Norway to visit them.

I had travelled to Kenya on February 7, 2019 to witness the birth of my second son who was born on March 5th 2019.

It had been an exciting few weeks in Kenya because we had just welcomed our second born Ammaar and adding a new member to our growing family was such a joy.

While in Kenya, we carried out the same traditional customs for Ammaar as we had done for Hamid, and our whole family was in a celebratory mood.

My life was perfect.

I had a beautiful, growing and healthy family that I was proud of. I had a good job in Norway and was able to provide for my family back in Garissa.

Life was good.

I was blessed and grateful to God for all His providence and mercies in my life.

Nothing was amiss.

Well, everything seemed to be okay, apart from the fact that Hamid had not been feeling very well. It appeared to just be the normal maladies that usually affect infants from time to time. He had not been eating well, and that was causing him to lose weight. But other than that, we really had very little reason for concern. To be on the safe side, Fardowsa and I had decided to have Hamid checked by a doctor just to make sure he was okay. We took him to Family First Medical Centre in Garissa, two times in February within a two-week span. The doctor who attended to us was Dr. Abdullahi, the same physician who had helped in the delivery of Hamid. Dr. Abdullahi found that Hamid had a high fever and was losing blood and gave him syrup for anaemia and vitamins to increase his blood level. It was a simple treatment and Hamid did fine for some days.

Nothing untoward.

After getting the anaemia medication and vitamins, I was confident that Hamid was on the mend and that he would be fine.

I could not have been more wrong, as I was soon to find out on that unforgettable 28th day of March when my wife called me frantically with the worst news I had never imagined I would have to hear.

I was in Norway, having returned back on March 17 and I had left Hamid doing well and eating normally, as was his younger brother Ammaar who was breastfeeding at the time.

So, when I got a call from Hamid's mother, I was not expecting an emergency. I just thought it was a routinely, normal call from my wife.

It was not.

"Hamid is very sick, and his condition is getting worse very quickly."

Fardowsa's voice crackled as she struggled to get the words out— her pain, disbelief, and fear zapped me through the phone.

The worried tone in her voice told me that things were very serious with Hamid.

I told her to take him to the doctor, which she did. She went back to the same hospital, Family First Medical Centre. They took some blood samples and also carried out a CT and Ultrasound scan on him. The samples were then sent to South Africa.

Now we had to wait to find out what was ailing Hamid. His condition was deteriorating quickly and everyone in the family was worried.

We needed to know the outcome of the tests quickly, so that we could figure out a way forward for his health.

We did not have to wait for too long. The results came the next day, on March 29.

Fardowsa called, this time with the extreme bad news.

"Hamid has been diagnosed with cancer. Kidney cancer!"

It is the most shocking statement I have ever heard in my life.

What? Who? Did I hear what I thought I heard? Or, a good perhaps, it was a dream?

Figure 3 gives X-ray images of Hamid's lungs.

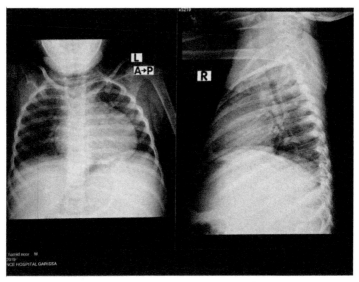

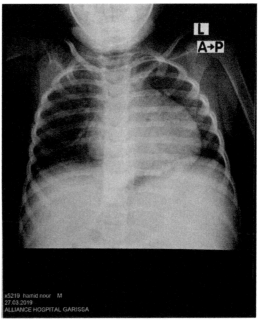

Figure 3: X-ray images of Hamid's lungs.

My mind started to spin.

My heart dropped to my feet.

I felt my mouth dry up immediately.

I was in complete, utter shock.

Staring unblinkingly at my phone like I had just seen a ghost, I gasped.

"What are you talking about?"

It was the only sentence that my mouth managed to formulate.

Fardowsa repeated the same words and, for a split second, I thought it was a joke. But I knew my wife well enough to know that she would never joke about something so grave. No sane person would.

Still, what she had just said seemed impossible. It made no sense in my brain. I had literally just seen Hamid back home in Garissa a few days ago— in fact less than two weeks ago — and he certainly did not look like a child who had something as violent as cancer ravaging inside his body.

So what did she mean? Perhaps I had misheard her. Was the phone connection not clear? Was it a case of poor network between Norway and Kenya?

Was it a dream? It had to be!

All these thoughts raced through my mind as I tried to make sense of what she had just told me.

Sadly, while it felt very nightmarish, it was not a dream and I was not dreaming. Everything was very real. I was very much wide-awake, albeit in shock, as Fardowsa struggled to calm herself enough to relay the incomprehensible news of our son's ominous diagnosis.

The results read by Dr. Abdullahi concluded that Hamid had Wilms tumour, which is a type of childhood cancer that starts in the kidneys. A very scary diagnosis indeed.

I was living a parent's worst nightmare, the worst type of nightmare that I could never wish on even the worst of my worst of enemies.

I could not grasp how such a seemingly healthy and very young boy could get cancer. Where did he get it from? Did he get it from his diet? Was it genetic? As far as I knew, no one from either side of the family had cancer.

Too many questions ran through my mind.

But now the loss of appetite and anaemia made sense. It had been cancer all along.

The doctors at Family First Medical Centre had told Fardowsa that Wilms Tumour was a typical form of cancer for children under the age of three and that as long as it was treated in good time, Hamid's chances of survival were high.

Despite the overwhelming fear and uncertainty, I had to remain strong and steadfast in my belief that my dear son would recover, especially for Fardowsa who was beside herself with sheer fear and feelings of uncertainty.

I quickly gathered myself together and consulted with my doctor in Norway. After speaking to him, I managed to calm down and decided to go and get my son from Kenya.

My son needed me now, more than ever, and his chances of survival would be much higher if he was treated in Norway than in Kenya, I reasoned.

In desperation, I called my mother Dalhid who also lived in Norway and, thankfully, she was strong enough and was able to calm my nerves.

We quickly discussed what to do and decided both of us to travel to Garissa to get Hamid and take him to Norway for specialized care.

I then went straight to my Oslo-based doctor and told him everything that had happened. I desperately needed his advice and knew that he would be in a better position to advise me on the best medical options available to me in Oslo. He agreed with me that Norway was the best option for Hamid at that critical moment. It was an emergency and every moment counted. I got the full information from my doctor and thanked him. I was grateful for his support at such a trying time in my life.

In the afternoon, on the same day of March 29, I hurriedly went to the travel agency to buy plane tickets. I bought a ticket for my mother and myself, as well as a one-way ticket for Hamid.

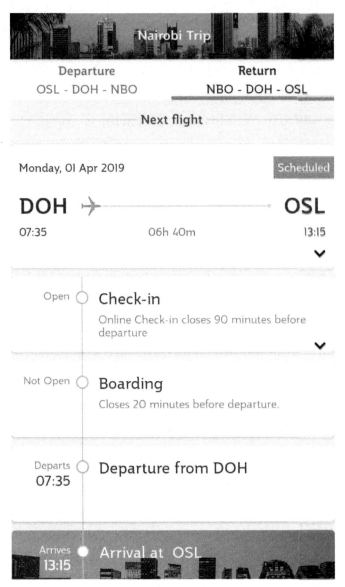

Figure 4: Picture of our three air tickets, from Oslo to Nairobi and Nairobi to Oslo.

The very next day, March 30 at 4 pm, we left Oslo for Nairobi.

I was not wasting any time.

We landed in Nairobi on the 31st in the morning.

Everything happened so fast. Within 48 hours of receiving the shocking news of my son's cancer diagnosis, I was already in Kenya with my mother, ready to bring him back to Norway with us.

Whatever happened from the moment we landed in Nairobi is still a blur to me. I did not have time to process all that was happening. In fact, I was on autopilot mode throughout. I had made the decision to only concentrate on the mission at hand, which was to collect Hamid and get him to a hospital in Oslo for high quality, specialized treatment.

I knew that if I were to stop and think about what was happening to my son, I would start panicking and I could not afford to do that. I had to be strong for my son, my wife, and my whole family but inside, I was a mess and maintaining a sober mind even as my world came crashing around me was not an easy thing to do.

Only God knows how I managed to maintain a calm demeanour through it all.

I had to focus on making all the arrangements while at the same time containing my emotions and anxiety, and it was the hardest thing that I have ever had to do.

You see, I had done my research on kidney cancer and what I had found out was enough to make any father worried. Wilms tumour is a rare type of kidney cancer that mainly affects children below the age of 3, and while the overall survival rates are 90% especially if the tumour is detected and treated in the early stages, death still occurs in a small percentage of cases[1]. This is particularly so if the tumour has spread to other parts of the body or if there are complications from treatment.

Therefore, while I was glad that the cancer had been detected early, I was still worried about Hamid being among those in that minority 10% who could possibly lose their life to Wilms tumour.

I, however, had to force myself to think positively. This was no time for a pity party or any type of negativity. Hamid needed me.

---

1   See: Servaes, S. E., Hoffer, F. A., Smith, E. A., & Khanna, G. (2019). Imaging of Wilms tumor: an update. Pediatric Radiology, 49, 1441-1452

He needed me fully focused, resolute, and fearless enough to be able to fight for his life with all my energy.

There was no time to waste. In my mind, every second that passed meant that Hamid's chances of survival were quickly diminishing.

As soon as we had landed in Nairobi at 8 am on March 31, the next step was for me to make my way to Garissa to get Hamid. Since Hamid was in Garissa and not in Nairobi, I took a flight to Garissa alone and left my mother in a hotel in Nairobi waiting for us.

At 2pm, I left for Garissa and at around 3pm, was met by Fardowsa, my mother-in-law and of course Hamid at the Garissa Airstrip. It was such an emotional reunion, and very ironic considering that the last time I had seen them, we had been in a celebratory period, celebrating the birth of my son. Now, we were meeting under highly stressful and unfortunate circumstances, with our son's life hanging in the balance.

Despite the fact that he looked weak, I was relieved to see Hamid. Seeing him alive gave me some sort of solace, comfort and strength.

Fardowsa was highly emotional, as I had expected her to be, and it was even worse because she had given birth only about 3 weeks ago and had not healed well.

Seeing her in that state broke my heart. I truly felt for her; her baby boy was deadly ill and there was little she could do to make him better.

There is no worse feeling for a parent than that feeling of helplessness. I understood exactly how she was feeling, but I had to be strong for her and our son.

At around 4pm, I had already taken Hamid together with my mother-in-law from the Garissa airstrip back to Nairobi where we arrived at 5pm and reconnected with my mother.

We made our way towards Jomo Kenyatta International Airport (JKIA) for our departure for Oslo, Norway at 8pm but when we arrived at the airport, we encountered a hitch that threatened to cut short our plans to travel back to Norway that night.

We were prevented from boarding the aircraft with Hamid since he was too weak and had an extremely high fever. The airport nurse, my cousin Mr. Abdiaziz Dubat Haret, came, checked on him, and finally, after what felt like an eternity, we were given the green light to board the plane thanks to the airport nurse and my cousin Abdiaziz. I am truly grateful to Abdiaziz for staying by my side at that time.

We then boarded the plane and departed for Oslo, Norway. Our flight back to Norway commenced at 11 pm.

I can't remember much about that flight except that I had wanted to make sure that Hamid was as comfortable as possible.

Once inside the aircraft, I was relieved to notice that Hamid was not as badly off as he had been earlier that day. He had improved quite a bit, thanks to the fact that we had Paracetamol and were giving it to him every 4 hours.

He had a fever, but thankfully it was not above 39°C so it was not critical.

He was, however, not his usual playful self. He was still not eating, nor was he playing like a normal kid would. He was in shock, having been separated from his mother for the first time ever in his life. He was a lot more accustomed to being with his mother than he was with me. He was not used to me because I lived and worked in Norway and, therefore, adjusting to being around me and not his mother was giving him a lot of separation anxiety. The pain from the fever was also weighing him down heavily and affecting his moods, plus his stomach had enlarged considerably, which was making him very uncomfortable.

As I looked at his innocent face and saw the suffering he must have been going through but could not articulate since he was too young to speak, I was more determined than ever that I would do everything in my power as his father to make sure he fully recovered from this cancer.

This horrid disease would not get the better of us.

I surely was not going to give up without a fight.

Tough times don't last, tough people do. We would weather the storm together.

I would make certain of that.

Wow! What a stressful, adrenaline-rushed day that had been. It felt like a movie, albeit a bad one. A horror movie actually.

We had spent less than 16 hours in Kenya!

I'm not sure where we got the strength and energy from but somehow, together with the help of Fardowsa and my mother-in-law, we had managed to coordinate everything with minimal hiccups.

To accomplish all of that in less than a day— flying to and fro Norway, with my mother and Hamid in tow, all within the same day— was no easy feat.

I am still in awe of what we did that day. It truly is a testament to the power of the mind, and what human beings can accomplish when we are determined. Truly, we can do anything that we put our minds to do.

Not saying that it was an easy day, though.

Nothing could be further from the truth.

Emotions had been running high all day. Fardowsa had been a wreck emotionally. She was beside herself with sadness and anxiety as she was getting separated from her baby for the time ever since his birth and letting him leave the country without her was the toughest thing she had ever been through.

The separation anxiety was real, and she had reluctantly allowed me to take him to Norway because we all agreed that Norway was the best and taking Hamid there was the most rational thing to do for his health, but that still did not make it easier for her to let him go.

Hamid too cried a lot when he was separated from his mother because he had never once been away from her in his entire life.

It was tough for me to see their anguish, but I had no choice. Fardowsa and Ammaar were not able to travel back with us to Norway since she had no visa at the time, and Ammaar had just been born so he had neither visa nor passport. Luckily for us, Hamid had a passport, which was ironically expiring only two months away in June.

I shuddered to imagine what our options would have been if he had no passport. Traveling to Norway at such a short notice without travel documentation would have been impossible, and this would have meant that I would not have been able to take

Hamid with me to Norway for treatment, and who knows what that would have meant for his fast-deteriorating condition.

I really thanked God that we had gotten him the passport shortly after his birth, just one and a half months later after he had been born. Had I not gotten his passport processed back then, it would have been very difficult to take him to Norway so quickly.

It felt as if God had known all along that we would desperately need it someday.

Chapter 2: Calm in the Storm

"In the midst of movement and chaos, keep stillness inside of you." — Deepak Chopra

2

April 1, 2019.

It was 2pm.

Hamid, my mother and myself landed in Oslo, Norway.

Unbeknownst to us, this is where Hamid would be calling home for the next 2 years of his life.

Without wasting any time or even being able to catch our breath, freshen up or eat, we took Hamid straight to the Oslo Emergency Hospital in downtown Oslo, also known as Legevakten.

Luckily, I at least had all the scans from Kenya so they wasted no time and called the Children's Cancer Emergency Department in Rikshospitalet, the biggest hospital in Norway. They referred us to Rikshospitalet, as it was the hospital that was best equipped to treat cancer, so Hamid stood a higher chance of successful treatment there.

In the meantime, they also took a small sample and we stayed at Legevakten for about 30-40 minutes.

About 1 hour after our arrival at Legevakten, we were on the move. Yet again.

This time, we took an ambulance to the Children's Cancer Emergency Department in Rikshospitalet, about 15 minutes' drive from Legevakten, and two nurses were ready to receive us by the time we arrived.

The nurses had been waiting for us in the parking lot, and as soon as we arrived, they immediately took Hamid to a bed in Room 3063 in Rikshospitalet that was prepared for us for check-up.

Figure 5: Our room in Rikshospitalet, where we spent most of our time while in hospital[2].

I was very pleasantly surprised by the care and concern that the staff at Rikshospitalet showed us, especially given the urgent circumstances and how frantic I was. They treated us exceptionally well throughout the whole process, even though they had never

---

2   Photo by Jasmin.

seen us before and only had the small bit of information that they had received from Legevakta.

At this point, Hamid's condition was stable, though he had a high fever and his energy was still low.

The doctors told me I had saved his life by bringing him so soon, and that chances of survival were higher the sooner the diagnosis was done.

I thanked God for granting us the wisdom in taking the urgent measures to save my first-born and for His being with us in this journey.

It had been a tornado of activity and a rollercoaster of emotions. But Hamid's life was worth every bit of it.

Very worth it.

****

At Rikshospitalet, our world was about to be shaken again.

The doctors verified that it was indeed cancer.

However, it was *not* Wilms tumour as we had been told in Garissa.

"What?!"

I could not believe my ears. That was really a shock to me.

Based on the sample that they tested, they discovered that while it indeed was a kidney-related cancer, just like Wilms tumour is, it was not, in fact, Wilms tumour.

Hamid had *Neuroblastoma.*

N-E-U-R-O-B-L-A-S-T-O-M-A.

"Neuro-whaaaat?"

I struggled to process this very long, mouthful of a word.

I'd never heard of it before and I had a really difficult time pronouncing it. All I knew is that it sounded very scary, and I, for sure, did not want my dear son to have any of whatever it meant.

Yet, I was relieved about getting a correct diagnosis. All the alternative scenarios started running through my mind. What if we had started treating the wrong cancer?

I thought about how they had gotten the diagnosis wrong, yet in Norway they had very quickly been able to get a proper diagnosis of what specifically was ailing my son.

Who knows what could have happened!?

It struck me like a ton of bricks just how important a correct diagnosis is.

It could mean the difference between life and death.

Literally.

That's when it dawned on me just how I had truly made the right decision to seek treatment in Norway instead of leaving Hamid to be treated in Kenya.

I shuddered to imagine what else they would have happen in Kenya, and what that would have meant for Hamid's chances of survival.

Luckily, that was something I did not have to deal with.

My son had just been confirmed to have Neuroblastoma, and that correct diagnosis was the first step in the right direction for Hamid's treatment.

At that moment, when they had told me the name of the cancer, I had no idea what it was. Now, I am among the most knowledgeable men on Neuroblastoma!

No kidding!

Having to deal with it so intimately forced me to become an expert on the subject.

To give you just a small overview of the disease[3], Neuroblastoma is basically a type of cancer that develops from immature nerve cells called neuroblasts. It usually affects infants like Hamid and young children, but can also occur in older children and adults in rare instances. Figure 6 shows origin and development of Neuroblastoma as well as the difference between Neuroblastoma and Wilms Tumour.

---

3   The information provided in this book was obtained from many
    sources. These have been acknowledged in various instances in this
    book. For further reading, see additional information on these in the
    Bibliography section at the end of the book.

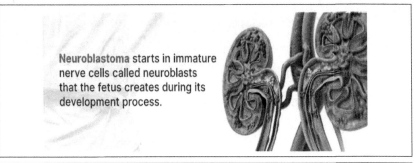

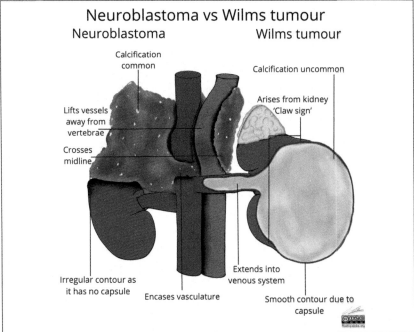

Figure 6: Origin spread in both Neuroblastoma and Wilms Tumour[4].

4   Sources: *Top image*: marijuanadoctors.com/conditions/
     neuroblastoma/
     Bottom image: https://radiopaedia.org/cases/93906/studies/112434?l
     ang=us&referrer=%2Farticles%2Fneuroblastoma-vs-wilms-tumour-
     1%3Flang%3Dus%23image_list_item_56149591

It is a rare cancer and its cause is not fully understood[5]. It most commonly originates in the adrenal glands, which are located on top of the kidneys, but can also develop in other areas of the body such as the chest, neck, pelvis or abdomen.

Symptoms of Neuroblastoma often include fatigue, low energy, a lump or swelling in the abdomen, chest, neck, or pelvis, bone pain, and unexplained weight loss.

When it comes to the treatment of Neuroblastoma, it really boils down to the stage of the cancer and may include surgery, chemotherapy, radiation therapy, and/or other types of treatment.

The prognosis for Neuroblastoma varies depending on the stage of the cancer, the age of the patient, and other factors.

There are three risk levels of Neuroblastoma:

- Low risk
- Intermediate
- High risk

5   https://www.cancer.org/cancer/types/neuroblastoma/treating/
by-risk-group.html#:~:text=Children%20at%20low%20risk%20
usually,go%20away%20on%20their%20own

Hamid had high risk Neuroblastoma and was therefore to undergo the more intense and advanced process of Neuroblastoma treatment that was likely going to include a combination of chemotherapy, surgery, and radiation therapy (such as MIBG radiotherapy).

Having done all this research on the disease, I now began to understand that the reason Hamid had been losing blood in Garissa was because it had been collecting at the entrance of the kidney area and had become meat-like in appearance, which was actually a Neuroblastoma tumor.

The loss of blood, appetite, low energy, and weight loss all had a name behind it- *Neuroblastoma*.

It was hard for me to process all this new information, especially considering that I had grown to accept that Hamid had Wilms tumor and I had done so much research on it, trying to figure out and familiarize myself with the disease.

Now, I had to reset my mind.

It felt like my world had been swept up in a whirlwind, a tornado of unexpected twists and turns that I never expected to go through in a million years, and having to keep up with all the information I was being bombarded with was a lot to deal with.

I was tired. I had just come from a less-than 48-hour rescue mission from Norway to Kenya and back, and had not even slept one wink.

I was exhausted, and mentally drained.

But there was no time to waste. No time to mull around and feel sorry for myself. Hamid had to be transferred to Rikshospitalet where he would get the best treatment for Neuroblastoma as soon as possible.

✳✳✳✳

Hamid was scheduled to start chemotherapy two days after arrival in Norway, on April 3, and over the next several months, he would be undergoing a battery of different treatment regimens, including surgery, radiation and immunotherapy at Rikshospitalet.

He was in for the hardest battle of his short life.

In the meantime, there was so much going on.

To say that it was chaotic would be the understatement of the year.

It was a whirlwind.

It turned out to be a period of establishing myself to enable me to take care of Hamid in the long-term under the most comfortable circumstances possible.

You see, I had been living with my mother in Norway so I had not needed much in terms of a living space, furniture and household items.

Now, I was supposed to be taking care of an ailing baby, as well as my wife and second born son both of whom would both be joining us in Oslo.

I had to buy a car and car seats for my two sons, rent a sizable house big enough to house my small family, a refrigerator, a washing machine, furniture, beddings, utensils and much more.

As this was going on, I was simultaneously working on Fardowsa's visa, which is always a long process, especially in Kenya.

During this process, I had to pay 3300 Norwegian Kroner (350 US dollars) to the Embassy for a DNA test to validate that Ammaar was really my child.

The positive result came back in mid-April 2019, and Fardowsa eventually got her visa on April 23.

Fardowsa also had to apply a passport for Ammaar as well as a Family Reunion Visa for herself.

She was to apply for a Family Reunion Visa from the Norwegian Embassy in Nairobi before she could enter Norway because she only had a 90-day visa. Otherwise, she would have had to leave Norway and apply for a Family Reunion Visa after staying in Norway for 90 days. So she had to stay in Nairobi a while longer after getting her visa and Ammaar's passport.

I applied for it on her behalf online, paid for everything, and then she took the signed documents to the Norwegian Embassy in Nairobi. It was only then that she was able to travel to Norway.

I am grateful that the Norwegian Embassy was very helpful in the whole process, and I am grateful to them till this day for all the assistance they gave me in processing my wife and son's travel documents.

I have to especially single out Lene Bjørgan, a clinical social worker in the Children's and Youth Clinic, Rikshospitalet. She was the one helping me to contact the embassy in Nairobi to process Fardowsa's and Ammaar's travel documents, while my friend Mr. Abdifatah Abass was in Nairobi helping Fardowsa and Ammaar in taking care of their paperwork needed in Nairobi and also taking them to the embassy physically. On April 12, Lene wrote a letter explaining the urgent need to have Hamid's mother present in Norway due to the gravity of his diagnosis. I sent the letter to the Norwegian Embassy in Kenya and this letter really helped to fast track the visa and passport process for Fardowsa and Ammaar.

I was handling and organizing this all between early April and the end of May, when my wife and second born were going to arrive.

At the same time, Hamid's chemotherapy had started on April 3 and was ongoing. In between this, the doctors were constantly assessing Hamid's blood tests, CT scans, ultrasound, MRI's, MiBG scans, PET scans (Figure 7).

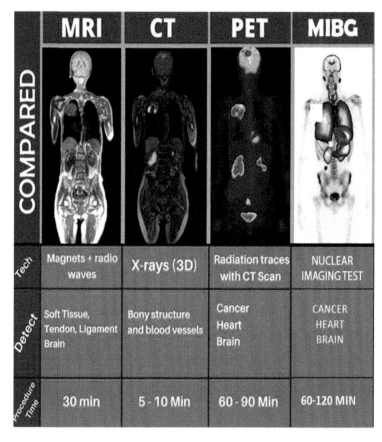

	MRI	CT	PET	MIBG
Tech	Magnets + radio waves	X-rays (3D)	Radiation traces with CT Scan	NUCLEAR IMAGING TEST
Detect	Soft Tissue, Tendon, Ligament Brain	Bony structure and blood vessels	Cancer Heart Brain	CANCER HEART BRAIN
Procedure Time	30 min	5 - 10 Min	60 - 90 Min	60-120 MIN

Figure 7: CT scans, MRI's, MiBG scans, PET scans[6].

There was no time to rest.

I have to say, though, that the biggest challenge in this entire adjustment period in Oslo was the fact that Hamid and I were practically strangers to each other up until this point.

6   Image source: https://bookmerilab.com/tests/ct-scan/pet-ct-scan/

We had never truly had the time to bond like father and son.

You see, since I worked in Norway, Hamid had spent all his life, all two years of it, in Garissa with his mother.

His mother, my wife's relatives, and the community in Garissa were all he knew.

He had never lived with me for more than a few weeks at a time, and every time I would go back to Garissa to visit them, it would feel as if we had to get reacquainted all over again due to the periods of time we would be away from each other, and his short memory span as a baby.

Now, on top of being extremely sick in his body, he was without his mother and familiar surroundings.

For the first time ever.

A new primary caregiver. New people. New Country. New culture. New language. Different weather. Constant trips and stays in and out of the hospital.

It was a lot!

And very chaotic, especially for such a young child.

Literally, a baby.

Having to deal with the type of turmoil and trauma that would cripple even the strongest of men.

I would sometimes look at his innocent face and my heart would break for him. Such a pure soul, dealing with so much pain that he did not deserve to go through at all.

It was a lot for me to witness as his father.

I am sure that it was very difficult for his young brain to process everything that he was going through. He just didn't have the language to express into words all of his distress and discomfort.

I deeply empathized with just how hard of an adjustment it was for him at such a young age, having to be abruptly disconnected from his beloved mother and the only community he knew, only to be brought to a new country with new people, new weather, and the constant barrage of treatments.

Neuroblastoma had torn him apart from the only life he had known.

And it was up to me to make sure his transition in this new phase of his life was as seamless and stress free as possible.

I had my work cut out for me.

I had to ensure that Hamid was as comfortable as possible, not only with me as his new caregiver, but also with living in a completely new country altogether and having to adjust to his new reality of having to constantly be under some medical treatment or another.

I did this, even as my plate was full with so many responsibilities- hospital visits, establishing myself and processing the visa and passport.

I was always by Hamid's side whenever he was admitted to hospital, and thankfully, my mother would accompany me as well, especially in the very beginning when Fardowsa was yet to arrive in Norway.

One of the hardest adjustments for me was taking care of Hamid when he was not in hospital.

Up until this point, I had never in my life taken care of a baby, so I had a lot of things to learn. This is why my mother was always with me, lending me a much-needed lending hand.

Changing his diapers. Brushing his teeth. Bathing him. Playing with him. Soothing and comforting him. Getting him to fall asleep.

It was all so new to me.

Taking care of a baby, and especially a sick one, is one of the challenging jobs one can ever do, especially for a man who is not used to household chores as I had also been learning from my wife when I would visit Garissa.

And boy, it was a lot of hard work, a lot harder than my regular job. So much so that I had to take leave from my job because there was no way I could possibly balance my work commitments with taking care of Hamid full-time.

Thankfully, my employer and the welfare system (NAV) were very supportive of me during this period, allowing me to take paid leave so that I could fully take care of my sick son without having to worry about paying the bills, which would have been a serious source of stress for me during such a trying time.

I have to commend the welfare system in Norway for being that mindful and caring for the welfare of workers. It is something that can be learnt and practised especially in other countries where "welfare" do not truly live to its name.

In Norway, healthcare is free and one is entitled to financial support from NAV (the Norwegian Labour and Welfare Agency) if they are looking after a child who is ill or injured, of course depending on the specific situation. In my case, Hamid was dealing with cancer, which is considered to be an extremely serious illness, and indeed it is.

Prior to this, I was completely unaware of the rights I had in Norway when it comes to taking care of a sick child. That was until the doctors brought to my attention my possible eligibility for sick allowance.

They asked me if I had been working for a duration of at least 3 months before Hamid became sick, and I answered in the affirmative. Then, they requested me for a printout of my last 3 months' payrolls, which I gave to them. They then graciously helped me fill in a form called *'Pleiepenger for Sykt Barn'* (translated into English, as "nursing allowance for sick children / caretakers").

After about a week or so, I got a response that I would be receiving an amount equal to the average of my last 3 payrolls.

After that, all I was required to do was fill in the Pleiepenger for Sykt Barn form every 3 months until January 2021. And that Hamid would also be getting assistance allowance throughout the period of his sickness.

This was a huge financial relief to me, a real weight off my shoulders, and I was free to focus fully on my son's recovery journey, instead of having to worry about taking care of my bills as well.

My family and friends helped to ease my burden as well.

I was not alone in this journey.

My mother, brothers and sisters all helped me in one way or another. I had 6 younger siblings - 3 brothers and 3 sisters - who lived in Norway, and it was amazing how they all came to us with all kinds of support, moral and psychological support, that helped my family settle down and be able to face the challenges during this trying period.

When I finally got an apartment, after much searching, my mother and siblings helped me buy furniture and all the much-needed household items since I could not leave Hamid alone in the hospital. Thanks to my family members, I was not as lonely as I could have been had I been completely on my own.

Those who could drive, like my brothers Ayanle, Shafi and Shukri bought things for the home, while my sisters Fadumo, Taman, and Roda helped to decorate, arrange and prepare the house before Fardowsa arrived in Norway. Roda, especially, brought wonderful gifts for Hamid in the hospital, while Fadumo and Taman were very helpful in preparing the house and bringing food to us in the hospital.

They would all regularly visit me, and truly made my apartment feel like a home with their presence and warmth.

49

Even my larger family back in Kenya was amazing in their support for me. My wife's side of the family was in shock when they got the bad news of Hamid's diagnosis. They were very close to Hamid, and were the ones who had been close to him back in Garissa, so you can only imagine the shock they got when they found out that he was in Norway for cancer treatment! It was difficult for them to adjust to the fact that they would not be able to see Hamid on daily basis as they had been used to.

They all tried their best to offer us, and especially my wife, all the moral support they could give.

What really moved me was how my family in Kenya would call Hamid and read the Quran to him, especially Mus'ab, my younger sibling in Kenya who organized children back home to read Quran for Hamid in their respective homes.

Such a touching gesture, and it would always put a smile on my face.

On top of the support of my family in Norway and Kenya, the medical staff in Oslo was simply incredible. Phenomenal! Throughout the various treatments Hamid had to undergo, we received a lot of support from the doctors and nurses, especially those in Rikshospitalet since they were the ones organizing every step of the treatment from chemotherapy to the stem transplant, including the logistics.

I am forever indebted to them.

I also received tremendous support from my bigger family in Europe. My big brothers and sisters, especially Mr. Bishar, Mr. Ibrahim, Mrs. Dahab all prayed with and for me, and also took the time to visit me in Oslo during this period. My uncle Abdiwahab from my mother's side and his son Mohamed who live in Europe also visited. This really warmed my heart since they had to travel all the way from their respective countries just to come see Hamid and I.

My neighbours and friends living in Oslo were amazing as well. The children of Ahmed Sanyare, my neighbour, who were also friends with my younger siblings, went out of their way to come visit Hamid and read the Quran to him. In particular, I must single out his son Abdullahi who organized his younger brothers and brought them to the hospital. They read the entire Quran to Hamid at different times. I was so touched by their gesture. They were not under any obligation or compulsion whatsoever, but they chose to do what they did on their own volition, and that showed me how much they genuinely cared.

Samatar, a good friend of mine from the Oslo Metropolitan University, used to come and visit me too, sometimes with his family.

Mind you, it is not as if I was calling people and telling them that I had a sick child. Nothing could be further from the truth. Somehow, word spread and people heard about it and they would reach out to me with their words of support.

This truly amplifies for me the importance of family and real friendship. A friend in need, is a friend indeed!

I am eternally grateful to all who showed their support in one way or another.

Nevertheless, despite all this support, I largely had to shoulder most of the work on my own, especially the emotional labour of dealing with a sick child. The emotional, mental and psychological turmoil was sometimes too unbearable for me to handle.

One of the biggest adjustments I had to make apart from taking care of Hamid was to create a strong bond with him considering the lack of proper bonding up until that point, so my number 1 goal was to win his trust.

Communicating with him in the beginning was such a challenge.

It was tough because he missed his mother dearly and would cry so much.

Knowing how to build a rapport with him was a steep learning curve for me.

I constantly had to soothe him and watch for any signs of distress, and then respond appropriately.

Given how precarious his health was, I was so afraid that something bad would happen to him, so I was always on the lookout for any signs of deteriorating health.

Any oversight could be fatal. Literally.

Overall, learning how to communicate with a baby who does not yet know how to speak fluently and has a limited vocabulary is no mean feat.

I had so much learning to do: speaking clearly, active listening, reflective listening, being considerate when he cried, and explaining feelings the best way I could were all aspects of communication that I was very deliberate about.

I remember constantly having to read guidelines online just so I could figure out how to effectively communicate with a two-year-old son.

It may have taken some time, but eventually, all that hard work finally paid off.

The invisible walls between us started to crumble, and he began to slowly trust me.

The crying lessened. The fussiness and lack of sleep reduced. His physical distance and detachment started to fade away.

We began playing together. Having fun together. Joking and laughing together. It was a thing of beauty to witness the walls come down and be replaced by an unshakable father-son bond that lasts until today.

A bond that I am sure will stand the test of time.

As the days passed by, and we spent all of our time together, Hamid naturally loosened up and we finally became close.

It was a beautiful struggle.

Through the chaos, confusion and adjustment to a new reality, Hamid and I were able to miraculously create our own little calm in the storm.

We somehow managed to grow closer and closer and to enjoy each other's company, and in the process we gave each other strength to fight another day. Being each other's support system.

Even at his young age, Hamid was such a strong source of encouragement to me, and I was constantly amazed at the level of strength and perseverance bottled up in his tiny, frail body.

While I would never want to go through such a health scare again, I look back at those days with a level of fondness, as they mark the beginning of a beautiful relationship between my first-born and I.

What a brave soul. A warrior and a survivor.

He is my hero.

Chapter 3: Culture Shock

"Through change of circumstances, the mettle of men is known." — Anonymous

3

May 28, 2019.

The day I had been waiting for had finally come.

Fardowsa and Ammaar arrived in Oslo.

Finally!

After close to two months of being busy processing their travel documents, they were here at last.

Safe and sound.

It had taken so long for them to arrive because the Norwegian Immigration informed us late that Fardowsa would also need to apply for a Family Reunion visa from Nairobi, in addition to the regular visa, before she could travel to Norway.

A Family Reunion visa is basically a form of long-stay visa for non-Norwegians who want to join a family member legally residing in Norway on a residence permit.

We had assumed that all she would need was her regular visa and passport only to find out that we had yet another hurdle to overcome.

And I had to handle the Family Reunion visa application as well.

Similar to any other travel document application, this was also an entire process that ended up taking about several weeks to complete, hence why they were only able to travel two months after Hamid and I arrived in Norway.

On May 26, my brother Ayanle had traveled to Nairobi for a trip of 24 hours to get Fardowsa and Ammaar and take them to Oslo after getting the 90-days visa and applying for the Family Reunion visa.

They all arrived in Oslo on the 28th.

At long last, they were here.

And I was over the moon!

Seeing them in the flesh was an amazing way to end my May.

This was the first time I had seen my wife and second born ever since returning to Norway with Hamid, and it felt like a lifetime had passed.

So much had happened – moving into a new apartment, furnishing the apartment, dealing with Hamid's treatment back and forth in between the hospital, and dealing with their travel document processing.

I barely had the time to breathe.

I was exhausted. Physically, mentally, and emotionally.

It had really taken a toll on me.

But with Fardowsa now around, I felt like a massive burden had been lifted off my back.

After all, a problem shared is a problem halved.

Despite having the assistance of my mother, siblings, friends and neighbours, nothing can replace a mother's love and nurturing.

Nothing.

There's just something about a mother's care that cannot be replaced by anyone.

And Hamid's excitement to be reconnected with his mother again after a two-month separation was all the proof I needed.

Initially, however, Hamid did not seem excited at all to see his mother. In fact, his first reaction was to cry, which really took me by surprise at first.

I had expected the opposite, considering how close they have always been.

What was going on? Why was he crying? Was he now scared of his mother, who he had previously been joined to the hip just two short months ago? Did he not miss her?

Well, it turns out that he simply did not recognize her at first. It hit me that he was still a baby, and babies have a very short memory span especially at such a young age.

Besides, he and I had bonded so quickly and had become so close, so much so that the initial distance between us had been replaced by a very close father-son attachment. We had spent literally every waking moment of our lives together for an entire two months, so it only made sense that his memory of his mother had started to fade.

Fardowsa tried to warm up to him but he kept on crying, and I'm sure that broke her heart. She had dearly missed him, and of course she had been very worried about him for a whole two months, constantly calling to find out how he was doing, and anxiously counting down to when they would finally be reunited.

All she wanted to do was to get into mama bear-mode and hug and protect her baby. But here he was crying, seemingly having forgotten her! And in such a short time too.

Thankfully, he eventually stopped crying and calmed down long enough to allow her to carry him.

What a relief.

I was concerned that she would have to go through the bonding process that I had been through for the past two months.

It turns out that he had been afraid of her because, by this time, after having gone through so many treatments, he had reached a point of assuming that everyone who was coming to our room was only there to administer injections to him.

Everyone was a suspect, I tell you! Hamid had grown to really fear injections.

But after 2-3 days of her warming up to him with no injections in sight, his memory appeared to be coming back and he realized that she was really his mother.

Seeing how Hamid eventually warmed up to his mom was heart-warming and I thought from there onwards, everything would be perfect for them in Norway.

Boy, was I wrong!

Little did I know the culture shock that was awaiting them, especially my wife.

✳✳✳✳

Fardowsa struggled to settle into her new life in Norway.

You see, Fardowsa has always just been a humble girl from the countryside.

Up until that point, Fardowsa had never been outside of the country. In fact, she had barely even been to Nairobi, the capital city of Kenya.

Most of her life had been spent in Garissa, and she was accustomed to the relatively slow, humdrum flow of village life. Waking up in the morning, doing the typical house chores, eating local food, and interacting with her village mates.

Her exposure to the modern trappings of urban, Western life was minimal and she had never even been on a plane before.

Just a simple girl from the village.

So you can only imagine the culture shock she experienced when she first arrived in Norway. Thrust into a completely new environment in a European country.

First of all, the experience of the flight was very nerve-wracking. Her first international flight, from Nairobi to Oslo, was a whopping 10 hours. That in itself was an incredible experience on its own, having to steady her nerves and the anxiety of being on such a long flight.

She could hardly sleep on the plane, and the plane food was so different from what she was used to.

After managing to calm herself down, she eventually arrived in Norway in one piece.

But that had just been the beginning of many other shocks to come her way.

As soon as the plane landed, she was about to encounter a series of other shocks.

Shock, after shock, after shock.

The first was the sheer newness of the Norwegian weather. The cold was such an affront to her system. As soon as the plane landed, she felt the immediate dip in temperature. It was not winter yet, but it was nearing summertime, but it was still cold to Fardowsa and Ammaar who were only used to Garissa's hot, sunny weather.

She had worn warm clothes but they were not nearly warm enough for the relatively cold Norwegian weather.

I had warned her about the cold obviously, but it's one thing to be told something and another thing entirely to experience it first-hand.

You can just imagine landing straight from the hot, sunny Garissa climate to having to adjust to the cold of a European country like Norway.

I eventually had to buy her heavier clothes because what she had come with just wouldn't cut it in Oslo.

She never got used to the clothes, though. She found them to be too big and ugly, in addition to being too heavy and difficult to wear. Even the kids struggled under the weight of the bulky clothing. They had gone from playing around in light t-shirts and shorts to the restriction of bulky jackets and pullover sweaters, woollen hats, and heavy socks and mittens.

Fardowsa particularly struggled to get used to what she saw other women in Oslo wear. As a Muslim from Garissa, the dress code for ladies is totally different from what women in Norway wear. She was used to seeing women covered from head to toe in their hijabs. So you can imagine her disbelief at seeing women dressing scantily in shorts, especially when exercising and jogging

66

outside, yet Fardowsa was freezing to the bone despite having a ton of clothes on!

This was quite a cultural shock. Norwegian women and Garissa women were polar opposites like Mars and Venus.

And it wasn't just the clothes. No. Fardowsa was also grappling with the overall shock of living amidst a completely different people, language and culture.

Seeing so many *'Wazungus'*[7] , all at once with their blue eyes and straight blonde hair was new to Fardowsa. She had been surrounded by Somalis and other Africans most of her life, so it was strange to all of a sudden be surrounded by white people when she had all along been used to the complete opposite.

And deciphering the nasally way white people speak was a new experience for her as well. In Garissa, Somali and Arabic is the language spoken by many, so she could only speak Somali, with a little sprinkling of broken Swahili here and there. She could not even speak English, and she certainly could not speak any of the languages commonly spoken in Norway such as Norwegian and Sami.

---

7   Swahili word for "White people"

Straight off the bat, therefore, Fardowsa had so many new things to adjust to. The language barrier, the cold weather, the heavy clothes, and the skimpy dress code of the native Norwegians was all quite a lot for her to process.

Fortunately, she did not have to make the adjustment all by herself. She had a support system available to her in the form of my sisters and the larger family in Norway. That's the beauty of having a family in a foreign country. Because I had my family near me in Norway, I had never ever felt isolated, despite being an African in a foreign country.

As soon as Fardowsa arrived, my sisters set about helping her to adapt to the system, teaching her the ropes of how things function in Oslo in terms of simple things like buying groceries, the currency, how to pay for things, and basic Norwegian words to help her manoeuvre her way through day-to-day life interactions.

"How are you?" – *Hvordan har du det?*

"Nice to meet you" – *Hyggelig å møte deg*

"Good morning" – *God morgen*

"Good afternoon" – *God ettermiddag*

"Good evening" – *God kveld*

"Goodbye" – *Ha det*

"Thank you" – *Takk*

"You're welcome" – *Vær så god*

"Please" – *Vær så snill*

"Excuse me" – *Unnskyld meg*

"Yes" – *Ja*

"No" – *Nei*

"I do not understand" – *Jeg forstår ikke*

"Where is ...?" – *Hvor er ...?*

"How much is the fare?" – *Hvor mye koster billetten?*

"One ticket to ..., please." – *En billett til ..., takk.*

"Store/shop" – *Butikk*

"How much does this cost?" – *Hvor mye koster dette?*

"Do you have ..." – *Har du ...*

"Do you accept credit cards?" – *Tar dere kredittkort?*

Those were the basic words and phrases Fardowsa had to learn in order to get by, and within the first few months, she had grasped most of them.

She, however, never quite managed to learn proper, in-depth Norwegian. There simply wasn't enough time.

As soon as she had settled, Fardowsa became consumed with taking care of Hamid so she was too busy, physically and psychologically, to learn a new language properly.

In any case, Fardowsa is an introvert and is rather reserved in terms of her personality. She has never been very outgoing, even in Garissa, so she kept her interactions with people at a bare minimum. Norwegians generally keep to themselves as well, so her being introverted was never an issue anyway.

Besides my siblings, my mother, and a few Somali friends, she hardly interacted with anyone, even our neighbours. Most of her life revolved around taking care of Hamid. The few times she did go outside, she would just go to the playground with the kids or visit my mother's house.

What helped was that my family in Norway used to live in our neighbourhood of Stovner Senter, and had been living there for about 10 years. We were very well known and popular in the neighbourhood.

Furthermore, our neighbours were mostly of foreign origin and not native Norwegians. Everyone in Stovner Senter, especially those of foreign origin, was friendly to Fardowsa since they knew that she was my wife.

It is a close-knit and friendly community and they had made her feel welcome straight away, so much so that she felt safe to move up and about even despite the language barrier.

One day when Fardowsa was going back home from the grocery store, a lady spoke to her but she did not respond since Fardowsa she did not understand Norwegian. She just kept on going and the lady also kept on calling her until Fardowsa could not ignore her anymore. The lady had become too loud and insistent that Fardowsa had to stop and pay attention to her.

The lady asked her, in Norwegian, where the kindergarten was. The lady was also new to the neighbourhood.

Unable to understand her words, Fardowsa just gestured to her that she could not speak Norwegian. To her surprise, the lady started conversing with her in Arabic, to which Fardowsa was able to answer her that she didn't know where the kindergarten was.

It was a funny moment, since it turned out that they both could speak Arabic even though neither of them initially knew that the other too spoke Arabic.

This is just one example of the many language barrier instances that Fardowsa had had to contend with in Norway.

Another thing I know Fardowsa really struggled with was the new food. The Norwegian food tasted so different to her and she never quite got fully accustomed to the new flavours and textures of food in Norway.

The fish, in particular, was not her cup of tea. At all! You see, fish is a staple in the Norwegian diet and it's typical to eat fish 2-3 times a week in Norway. In Garissa, however, it is a rarity.

She also strongly disliked sea crabs, and she would always remark about how the butter on the bread did not taste like the Blueband margarine in Kenya.

And to make things even worse, a lot of the food in Norway is packed in tins unlike in Kenya where most food is fresh. She never could wrap her mind around the idea of eating food from tins!

Shopping was by far the most challenging activity my wife had to figure out. In Garissa, we do not have malls as big and modern as the ones in Norway, so getting around the huge malls was an uphill task for Fardowsa.

Since she had quickly grasped the basic words she needed in order to shop, she decided to make an effort to do a bit of shopping at the mall. She would mostly buy simple food items and the things that she was already familiar with from back home such as milk, bread and eggs as well as the ones she could decipher from the labels on the products.

Considering that everything has a price tag, the shopping experience was relatively straightforward and she quickly learnt how to use a Visa Card. When the cashier scanned her shopping, she would just look at the screen and see the amount of money she needed to pay and pay it either with the card or in cash.

Soon enough, she become a pro at shopping and generally getting around using the local means of transportation.

However, she would get lost so many times! That was the main challenge with shopping. The malls in Oslo are so big that she would often get lost when getting in and getting out of the mall. While inside the mall, she could also not find the grocery shop numbers a lot of the time, and that would be such a big source of frustration to her.

And getting lost in malls was not even the worst that happened to her.

Oh no. There is one scary experience I distinctly recall with Ammaar. He got lost one day, giving us the fright of our life and sending us all into a near panic!

On this particular day, Fardowsa was in the house and, suddenly, Ammaar disappeared, nowhere to be seen. She started looking for him everywhere in the house, moving everything out of the way and checking for him in every nook, crook and cranny of the house in vain. He was gone. Disappeared into thin air.

I was terrified, because I had heard countless stories of babies falling from balconies or suffocating in cribs, and it was unusual for him to be so deathly quiet.

And as all parents know, it's ominous and makes us very afraid, whenever children become quiet.

Fardowsa was beside herself with terror. We were in the middle of dealing with Hamid's health crisis and could not bear to deal with yet another tragedy.

Had she neglected our second born in the midst of all of the hullabaloo with Hamid's back-and-forth treatment?

Thankfully, she were soon to find out that Ammaar had not disappeared at all. She had all along been holding him on her side!

Our near tears and fright gave way to laughter. It was so causing that she had been looking for a child who had literally just been with us all along.

But as relieving and funny as it was in that moment, it exemplified how Fardowsa had been feeling ever since arriving in Oslo. She had been in a state of constant worry over Hamid's condition that she could not fully relax.

The kids, on the other hand, were seemingly unaffected. Hamid had fully acclimated to life in Norway, and Ammaar was still very young, so he was not even aware of his new surroundings. To him, Oslo was just another place like any other.

After all, children typically find it easier to adjust to new surroundings than adults do, so the new environment did not affect him in any noticeable way.

All in all, Fardowsa was the one who was significantly impacted by the new life in Norway but she eventually got used to it.

Her focus, and our focus as parents, was 100% on Hamid's recovery. That was all that matters.

And what an overwhelming recovery process it would turn out to be!

Chapter 4: The Long Road to Healing

"And when I am ill, it is [God] who cures me." — (Ash-Shu'ara (Quran: 26:80) (A supplication of Prophet Abraham)

4

April 3, 2019.

The day Hamid started chemotherapy.

It was just 3 days after Hamid arrived in Oslo.

The day I had been dreading ever since his cancer diagnosis.

Chemotherapy is an extremely gruelling cancer treatment, even for adults, so I was very worried about the impact it would have on a tiny, frail body such as Hamid's.

Hamid would have to undergo chemotherapy treatment at Rikhospitalet for about two months, until late June 2019, after which he would undergo an operation.

The chemotherapy was necessary a matter of urgency, primarily as an acute life-saving measure to prevent the tumour from destroying vital organs and to shrink it for later surgery and other treatments.

The type of chemotherapy he went through is known as "Rapid COJEC."[8] Rapid COJEC (given in Figure 8) is a combination of five agents (cisplatin, vincristine, carboplatin, etoposide and cyclophosphamide) that is delivered directly into a child's bloodstream through their central line.

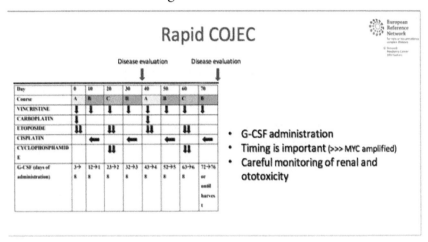

Figure 8: Rapid COJEC[9].

The therapy is administered in eight cycles separated by intervals of ten days and is completed within 70 days of the first treatment (see the diagram above). In high-risk patients, the use of Rapid COJEC is to give high doses of chemotherapy over a shorter time, which may improve survival.

---

8   "Rapid COJEC" as well as the technical information provided in this chapter were obtain from, among other sources: https://siope.eu/media/documents/escp-webinar-22sept-slides.pdf.

9   Image source: https://siope.eu/media/documents/escp-webinar-22sept-slides.pdf

This Rapid COJEC chemotherapy treatment is the first part of a treatment protocol that is known as the 'HR-NBL-2 Protocol,' which is used in 28 countries in Europe for the treatment of Neuroblastoma. The protocol consists of a number of treatments including Rapid COJEC, intensive induction chemotherapy, peripheral blood stem cell harvest, the excision of the primary tumour, peripheral blood stem cell rescue, radiotherapy to the site of the primary tumour and immunotherapy.

We were privileged to have the Chairman of the Protocol and the Head of Neuroblastoma in Norway, Dr. Ellen Ruud, as part of the team involved in Hamid's treatment. Dr. Ruud was the one getting reports from the doctors and the reference person, which was a great blessing to us.

Hamid's case was being handled by some of the very best doctors in Norway!

What an honour that our son's case was being handled by Europe's finest!

Having the best specialist on Neuroblastoma treating our son was a source of relief and reassurance to us since we knew that Hamid was being taken care of by the very best in Europe. Nevertheless, it did not mean that it was an easy process.

On the contrary, Hamid's chemotherapy was the hardest thing I have ever had to go through as a parent. The effects of the chemotherapy were quite devastating to witness. Almost immediately, Hamid started losing his hair. His head was punctuated with blotches of hair spots and his small lips were also bruised with sores, which was quite a traumatizing sight.

He was also constantly tired, weak, and sickly. He literally had no appetite anymore and had to be fed through a nasogastric tube (NG tube) otherwise he would have no nutrients in his young body. He also experienced periodic diarrhoea, and so it was important that he was well nourished and dehydrated.

It was brutal.

During this chemotherapy period, he was in and out of Rikshospitalet where it was being administered.

The chemotherapy was carried out over a course of many rounds, from April to late June. Once the chemotherapy treatment was over in late June, Hamid had yet another brutal treatment to go through - an operation!

Typically, after chemotherapy is carried out to shrink a tumour and stop its spreading, an operation is then done.

The operation took place on July 16 and was done to remove the tumour. Hamid had a pretty big tumour on the left side of his abdomen.

It had to be removed immediately.

During the operation, the left kidney, spleen, parts of the colon, and pancreas tail were also removed, in addition to the tumour,

Thankfully, the operation went well and he was strong enough to walk one week after the operation.

The operation was then followed by a stem cell harvest, known in medical terms as the Peripheral Blood Stem Cells (PBSC) harvest. Hamid was scheduled for a HDC (High Dose Chemotherapy) treatment in August and before then, his blood stem cells needed to be harvested. The HDC treatment was to involve the administration of high-dose chemotherapy and targets selected cells that have rapid growth/cell division, with cancer cells and blood stem cells being among these.

So, his blood stem cells had to be saved so that he could store them and get them back after the HDC treatment so as to use them after the high-dose chemotherapy had killed all the blood cells in his body, in addition to the target Neuroblastoma cells.

In high-risk Neuroblastoma treatment, based on the HR-NBL1 Protocol, a patient's own stem cells are used for treatment. To harvest his stem cells, the doctors took bags of his blood and were supposed to have stored two bags. In Hamid's case, however, they only managed to harvest one bag instead of the recommended two bags.

Once the stem cells were successfully harvested, Hamid underwent the HDC and stem cells transplant in August 2019. HDC drugs are a form of chemotherapy that work by blocking the DNA that helps cancer cells grow. They also help genes that are involved in cell growth work the way they should.

During the high dose therapy, a very high dosage of chemotherapy (busulphan and melphalan) is administered. Since the therapy is harmful to the bone marrow, a patient's own stem cells must be removed and stored. These stored stem cells are then returned to the patients after the high-dose treatment.

The harvesting of Hamid's stem cells, coupled with the high dose chemotherapy treatment, all took place in August and he was given back his harvested stem cells.

It was during this HDC treatment process that the complications began.

The unexpected happened. One of the scariest things no parent should ever have to deal with.

Just as the reality of his overwhelming treatment process was sinking in, were confronted by yet another unthinkable challenge.

Hamid, who was in the ICU, went into a coma!

The date was August 23, 2019.

One of the *darkest* days of my life.

To say that we were scared is an understatement.

You can imagine that Hamid's health was already severely compromised from the chemotherapy and operation, and now he had to deal with this!?

We were mortified.

I could not understand how or why this had happened.

The doctors told us that the CVC (central venous catheter) line, also known as a central line (c-line) (a line that medicine is given through), had become infected and was to be removed and replaced with a new one. A very serious and life-threatening infection was the cause. It is a very typical and predictable complication of high-dose treatment when you do not have a strong immune system for a considerable period of time. That is why doctors give back the blood stem cells that are not affected by the chemotherapy. It is a brutal treatment, but lifesaving.

In the process of replacing it with the new one, the oxygen pipe in his mouth bent without the knowledge of the doctors.

On top of that, the doctors had also first injected the wrong vein when they had first placed the CVC. All this, and the fact that he was already weak because of the HDC, is what had caused him to slip into a coma.

I was simply dumbfounded.

As if things could not get any worse, they had.

Terribly worse.

When it rains, it pours, they say. However, I could never have imagined in my wildest dreams that I would ever have to endure such an unrelentingly brutal downpour of rain in my own life. Things seemed to be going from bad to worse, and I could hardly process it all.

It was just too much for me to bear.

Not only did my very young and fragile son have cancer, he was now in a coma!

And there was no telling what would happen to him.

Heart pounding with fear and desperation, my mind churned with unanswered questions. How had this all happened? Was it something I had done or failed to do? Was this God's way of punishing me for something I had done?

Was my precious son going to be okay?

I had never felt so helpless in my entire life. So very hopeless. My world was crashing down around me as I tried to come to terms with the gravity of the situation and there was seemingly nothing I could do about it.

The coma lasted for a week, and during that week, everything was a blur.

All we did was wait, pray, and hope to God that everything would be okay.

Thank God he came out of the coma after a week.

It was such a relief!

But that relief turned out to be short lived.

Just a month later, on the 22nd of September, Hamid slipped into a coma again!

I could not believe it.

This time, the coma was brought about by an infection in the CVC and a high fever after the doctors were trying to change the CVC.

Hamid's cortisol levels were less than needed in his body, and the doctors had not been aware of that.

From that day onwards, the doctors were extremely cautious every time Hamid was to get the CVC or was going into the anaesthesia.

This notwithstanding, I clearly recall how careful they were, to the point of giving him a boost of cortisol before putting him under anaesthesia and carrying out the surgery for the CVC.

I owe the doctors a huge debt of gratitude for the care they consistently gave Hamid during these difficult and uncertain times.

The doctors and nurses were acutely aware of everything that was happening and treated Hamid with laser sharp focus.

They were cognizant of the pain that I, my wife, and my entire family were going through and were very kind and helpful to us.

The nurses gave us a hotel room inside the hospital that Fardowsa and Ammaar and me could stay in during the time we were in hospital and feel at home.

The hotel served us with a lot of care and love. This greatly helped to ease the emotional burden and mental anguish we were going through.

This second time around, Hamid remained in coma for two weeks. This was longer than the first time. He came out of it on October 6, 2019.

It was very difficult to understand why Hamid was becoming so susceptible to comas.

However, the doctors explained to us that after the HDC treatment, Hamid had become too weak, even weaker than he had been when he was getting chemotherapy in April. The weakness brought on by HDC was so severe, which is why he had ended up in the ICU two times; once in August and the second time in September.

In November 2019, a month after coming out of his second coma, Hamid started local radiation therapy at Radium Hospital in Oslo for a period of about three weeks. The purpose of the radiation was to kill the probable last tumour cells that were left in the primary tumour area. The radiation was basically beamed on to the site of the primary tumour area where Hamid's tumour had first been located.

****

January 2020.

The New Year started with the next phase of the treatment.

Hamid did not even have any time to truly celebrate the New Year. We welcomed the New Year at home, with Hamid only managing to view the fireworks from our living room window.

In this phase of the treatment, the doctors started Hamid on Vitamin A and immunotherapy, which was administered to him for six months, from January to June 2020.

Vitamin A inhibits cell division and is given together with immunotherapy (GD-2 antibodies) to increase the effect. GD-2 antibodies are signalling substances that sit on the remaining Neuroblastoma cells. The treatment is administered to help kill the last remaining cancer cells.

GD-2 antibody treatment was a relatively new practice by the time of Hamid treatment, and was, additionally, an extremely expensive treatment amounting to millions. The doctors have spent many years seeking approval for its use in treatment from the public in Norway.

Side effects of the immunotherapy are very common and can be very serious. Hamid was extremely lucky that he didn't get that much side effects from the treatment.

For the 6 months, Hamid took Vitamin A capsules intermittently– two weeks on, and two weeks off. During the two weeks that he took Vitamin A, he stayed at home, and then when he was off, he stayed in the hospital for the GD-2 antibody. So for six months, he therefore shuttled back and forth home and hospital, depending on whether he was on or off the vitamin.

Throughout Hamid's entire treatment process, we never left his side.

He was shuttled back and forth between Rikshospitalet, Akershus University Hospital (AHUS), and Radium Hospital depending on the particular treatment he was getting at any given time.

It was a very tough period for all of us when Hamid was in and out of hospital, for one form of treatment to the next, but we knew that we had to persevere and be strong for his sake.

Hamid needed us to be strong.

I can only imagine how exhausted he must have been through it all.

He was constantly on the NG tube and CVC for feeding and medication; otherwise he would have been severely undernourished.

Fortunately, the doctors were very vigilant about his nutrition. Even after he had been taken off the NB-tube, the doctors at AHUS recommended a very helpful and effective nutrition programme to ensure that Hamid ate normally and received adequate nourishment.

From April until about late October 2019, Hamid did not have a regular stay at home. Most of his time was present in and out of hospital because he was going through the chemotherapy, operation of his tumour, the HDC, the local radiation therapy, and the immunotherapy back to back with no rest at all, on top of having to recuperate from his comas.

There was always something happening.

We hardly even slept.

I am grateful to my mother, because she was there for us unwaveringly, every step of the way.

She was with me in hospital on most days. In the beginning, my mom and I were sleeping in the hospital, both in Rikshospitalet and AHUS. She was very worried and wanted to make sure she was there in case of anything.

However, when Hamid's condition started to improve and he began responding to the treatments, she felt more comfortable leaving me with Hamid. She would sleep at home and come to be with us during the daytime.

During the whole treatment period, I did not have a predictable routine or schedule.

Every day was different.

On those days when Hamid was extremely sick, I rarely ever slept. When he was not so sick, however, my routine was pretty regular. I would wake up at 09.00 or 10.00 or the nurse would wake me up. I would do my morning prayers and prepare myself. Then I would brush Hamid's teeth while he was in bed, since he did not leave his bed much.

I would then have breakfast in my room and plan with my wife and mother how the day would be, according to the shape Hamid was in on any given day.

On those days when Hamid could stand and move around, and if the weather was good, we walked with Hamid outside in the hospital compound and even played with him. Those were, by far, the best days in that gloomy period, and I was always glad to see Hamid walking and playing around happily instead of being cooped up in his hospital room all day long.

When he was unable to walk, we simply stayed inside.

Normally in Norway between April (when Hamid first came to Norway) and late September, the weather is great, warm and sunny, but from October to March, it's snowy and cold. So from October to January, we rarely took him outside for a walk.

Hamid's condition fluctuated tremendously during the whole period.

On some days, he would be strong and energetic, which would give us so much hope and encouragement, and other days, he would be so weak that he could barely open his eyes.

When he was not very sick, he could do normal things like standing up, going to the toilet in our room, and even brushing his teeth.

When he could eat, I would feed him with whatever nutritious meal and healthy foods like a slice of orange that he could manage to eat as prescribed by the doctors. I was very excited on those days because he could at least taste something with his mouth instead of being fed through the NG-tube.

This was very important to me because I did not want him to forget the taste of food and how to chew and swallow.

On other days when he was especially feeling stronger, we would play inside the room. We got a yoga mat from the nurse and would play on it.

During the snowy season, we were mostly inside and would play various indoor activities inside the hospital building. We would always find simple things to do to keep Hamid's mind preoccupied and away from the painful treatments he was getting.

Hamid always enjoyed these simple things.

I remember how he, in particular, developed a great fascination with birds whilst in hospital. The birds would perch on the windows, and he used to love seeing them there. He also liked chasing after birds outside on those few occasions when we went to the compound.

Sometimes, he would even get entertainment from the nurses and other hospital staff. I recall once how they brought clowns to cheer him up. That was a funny day, because he was terrified of the clowns! Hamid had never seen a clown before, so the sight of the clowns with their colourful and scary painted faces frightened him to no end.

He, however, did eventually warm up to them with time after getting used to their appearance and even became friends with them in the end!

They were such a source of joy and mirth for him inside those four walls.

He also made friends with the nurses and would often play with them. The nurses loved him, and he loved them. Being friends with the nurses was great for Hamid since he was not allowed to meet other kids in the hospital since he had tested positive for a MRSA bacterial infection and the hospital did not want to spread the infection around the hospital.

The interactions between him and the nurses always warmed my heart. I am so grateful that he was under their care; I could not ask for anything better!

Nonetheless, the treatment experience was tough on Hamid.

Apart from the harsh treatments in the form of chemotherapies and surgery, he really struggled with other things whilst in hospital.

Adjusting to being in a hospital room for months on end is not easy for a baby, especially one like Hamid who had been used to the freedom and simplicity of life in Garissa.

You have to remember that he was new to Norway so everything was very foreign and strange to him. Things like seeing sports cars in the hospital, for instance, were very new to him.

He had never been exposed to them.

He particularly struggled with the food. He had to get used to Norwegian food, which is very different from the food he was accustomed to in Garissa. His appetite was already low due to all the treatments he had to go through. The fact that he was mostly getting nourishment through the NG-tube worsened his already poor appetite.

Getting used to the Norwegian diet on top of all those feeding challenges was not easy at all for Hamid.

Thankfully, he only took liquid food through the NG-tube until late March 2021. Late March is when we removed the NG-tube and he was finally able to eat regular, solid foods through his mouth.

It was such a wonderful feeling as a father to see him eating normally again.

By mid-2020, Hamid's long stays in the hospitals had started to reduce and he started to spend most of his days at home when he was not getting in-patient treatment. This was a huge relief for all of us.

It allowed him to get a taste of home and family life and made his recovery process a lot easier and smoother.

In June 2020, as the Vitamin A and immunotherapy treatment was coming to an end, we received the best news since the start of Hamid's treatment protocol.

We received the good news during a meeting with the lead specialist Ellen Ruud on June 2020 Dr. Ellen informed us that he had no more signs of Neuroblastoma in his body.

Hamid was cancer-free!

Wow! This was music to my ears.

It was one of the happiest days of my life.

You can only imagine the jubilation and joy we felt when we got the news.

All the many dark days of tears, sleepless nights, and worries were finally over. All the days of wondering whether we were fighting a losing battle had finally come to an end.

It was over.

Hamid was healed, and we were overjoyed.

Over the moon.

I was grateful to God, the doctors, my family, and all our friends who had contributed to Hamid's recovery.

I could never have made it through the storm without them and I am forever indebted to everyone who stood by me during this difficult season in my life.

The good news was, however, followed by some bad news– Dr. Ellen warned us that the cancer could come back in one or two years so we had to be cautiously optimistic.

The good news, though, was that if the cancer did not return after two years, his chances of surviving would increase every year thereafter.

For the rest of 2020, Hamid was done with the treatments and medication but we still had to take him for regular check-ups to ensure that he was doing well and that if anything was detected during the check-ups, the doctors would be able to contain it in good time.

One of his last check-ups was done on his eyes, ears, nose and his teeth, all of which are susceptible to chemotherapy side effects.

Thankfully, all was well.

He was in good condition and all his organs were okay.

Moreover, he was a lot stronger than before and had started to stand firmly.

He was not back 100% but was a lot better than before.

It was a miracle.

My son was back!

He was doing so well that he did not have to take any more medication apart from Penicillin V, which he still takes twice every day till today, in the morning and evening, to protect him against pneumococcal bacteria attack. This is because his spleen was removed, and the bacteria can cause very serious infections in children. He will have to take it until he's around 15 years of age but other than that, he does not take any more medication or any other treatment.

By the end of 2020, Hamid was strong enough to travel.

In January 2021, we left Norway for Kenya.

Ready to start a new chapter of our lives in a new country as a healthy family.

That terrifying chapter was all behind us and we were beyond excited to create a new life in our beloved nation of Kenya.

I could not wait.

Chapter 5: The Rainbow after the Storm

"Sometimes the greatest storms bring out the greatest beauty. Life can be a storm, but your hope is a rainbow and your friends and family are the gold." — Steve Maraboli

5

January 8, 2021.

The day we left Norway for Kenya.

Fardowsa, Hamid, Ammaar, my mother and I.

What an exciting day that was!

The flight left at 16:30 and we arrived in Nairobi the following day in the morning.

It was almost exactly two years since Hamid had left Garissa for Oslo for his treatment process, and so, as you can imagine, a lot had changed during that time.

Hamid was about to turn four years in a few days' time, while Ammaar was just two months away from turning two years.

We had made the decision to return to Kenya mainly because Fardowsa and the kids were used to live in Kenya before they came to Norway, and we had only been in Norway for Hamid's treatment which had come to an end.

Fardowsa missed Kenya, and wanted to come back to where she really felt at home.

Kenya is our home, and it is where we had always wanted to raise our sons, so once Hamid was done with the full treatment process, we thought it was time now to return home.

East or west, home is best.

Nothing was keeping us in Norway.

My mother was not relocating to Kenya though. She only accompanied us during the journey to give us all the help we needed and to ensure that we settled back in Kenya seamlessly. She stayed in Kenya for just a few months and went back to Norway.

Out of all of us, Fardowsa was without doubt the most excited one to return to Kenya.

The immense joy she felt upon landing in Nairobi was beyond description.

Fardowsa had been very homesick ever since she landed in Norway so she was very relieved to be back home. All her family members live in Kenya and it had been very hard for her to adjust to life in a foreign country, even after two years of living there.

Despite a little bit of apprehension on my part, it turned out that adjusting back to life in Kenya after being away in Norway for those two years was not difficult at all.

All of us fit right back into the swing of things.

It was like we had never left in the first place.

Luckily, Hamid and Ammaar were still very young so they adjusted very well to life in Kenya. After all, Ammaar had only been a mere infant of two months old when he left Kenya, so he did not know much.

Hamid too had only been a baby.

Surprisingly, Hamid could remember a few people and places here and there, despite the two-year time away.

Our easy adjustment to life in Kenya was mainly because Fardowsa's entire family lives here and they welcomed us back with open arms, making the transition into the new life very seamless.

Our entire family was very excited when we arrived back.

They had been worriedly sick for the two years we had been away, and had constantly enquired about his progress, so when we told them that he was cancer-free, they were simply ecstatic.

Hamid's recovery was like a miracle to them.

The moment they laid eyes on him when we arrived, they were overjoyed. After two years away, seeing him again and in relatively good health was a thrill.

They were also excited to see Ammaar who had changed quite a bit as you can imagine, from a two-month old infant to a two-year old baby who had started to walk and talk.

They had not been privileged to see him grow up and had only seen glimpses of him through the photos and videos we would send back home from time to time.

The biggest source of concern for everyone when we settled in was Hamid's appetite and feeding habits.

In the beginning, he was not eating well at all, especially from January to March when we first got to Kenya. Just like in Norway, he was still struggling to eat normally and I recall how long he would take to complete just one meal.

The effects of the chemotherapy on his organs were still plaguing him, and we had to be patient as his body slowly rejuvenated.

Thankfully, he was not put on any special diet, as this would have been difficult to sustain in Kenya.

Till today, he eats what everybody in the family eats. However, we do make a point of giving him some extra carbohydrates and protein-rich foods since we want him to gain weight and muscle for strength.

Slowly but surely, his appetite has been improving over the months, something we are grateful for.

One thing we have been keen about in Kenya is ensuring that he goes for periodic check-ups just to make sure everything is okay with his health. We had been warned that Neuroblastoma can recur and there is no need to take any chances.

Better safe than sorry.

He has an oncologist in Gertrude's Hospital in Nairobi that monitors his progress, Dr. Doreen Karimi. Dr. Karimi normally takes Hamid's blood samples and sometimes refers him to Aga Khan Hospital for MRI scans, which Gertrude's Hospital doesn't offer.

The doctors and nurses at Gertrude's Hospital have been wonderful and I am grateful to them for helping to monitor Hamid's health in Kenya post-recovery.

Thankfully, Hamid rarely falls sick and those check-up results always come out clean, much to our relief.

Apart from the normal illnesses that children his age experience, he has been doing well and even plays with his younger brother like a normal child.

In fact, the biggest challenge he has had with his health so far occurred recently in March 2023 when he got measles and had a very high fever coupled with aches and pains. Even then, he recovered after 3 weeks and has been well ever since.

Other than that hiccup, his recovery has been remarkable.

He is as strong and energetic as other children his age, which is unbelievable considering just how dire his health condition had been.

The only milestone he has yet to achieve is going to school.

He hasn't started regular school yet but he did start home-schooling and has been doing well with his learning. He has even started reading and writing, which is been a huge, priceless milestone both to him, the whole family and me.

I am so proud of his progress and cannot wait to see how well he does once he officially joins school.

It's great to have him around his family in Kenya. I have no doubt that the warm weather, fresh food and family life has done his health a world of good. Every time he makes even the slightest bit of progress, I am happy with the decision we made to bring him back to Kenya.

There have been so many small wins, joyous moments and milestones that have shown just how much Hamid has improved ever since we arrived in Kenya. The biggest source of joy, nevertheless, was when he started becoming healthy, eating and running like a regular child.

For two years, the 'normal' things that other parents consider normal and take for granted were not normal for Hamid, so seeing him living a normal life has been the greatest source of happiness for Fardowsa and I.

I never take it for granted whenever we can go out with him and enjoy fun activities together such as visiting places like Nextgen Mall and Karura Forest in Nairobi.

Seeing his face light up in those moments is lights joy in me as a parent.

Overall, Hamid's post-recovery journey has been nothing short of a miracle.

The greatest source of joy for our family.

Hands down.

From almost losing his life, to making an almost 360° turnaround to where he is now, has been an astonishing episode to witness.

Sometimes I watch Hamid playing outside with his brother and friends without a care in the world and I can't help but marvel at just how far he has come.

Seeing how far has progressed and grown in two years never fails to amaze me and warm my heart.

It's been a breath-taking experience.

A testament that nothing in life is too hard to overcome and that no trial is too hard to prevail over. It speaks to the truth that no barrier is too difficult to surmount.

If Hamid was cured, anything can happen!

I am now firmly the biggest believer in the world, that anything is possible with God.

In fact, very few things faze me nowadays.

No matter what challenges I sometimes face from time to time, I rarely get worried. I rest assured that God has my back.

After all, can anything compare to almost losing a child to cancer?

If God could heal my son, He can do anything else.

Not just for me, but for you as well.

The miracle that happened with my son and family can be your story as well. No matter what situation you find yourself in.

With faith, family and persistence, all things are possible.

Always remember– the rainbow after your storm is on the other side of your faith. Just believe.

Never give up.

Keep on pushing!

Chapter 6: Lessons Learned

"It's not what happens to you, but how you react to it, that matters." Epictetus

6

It's June 2023.

And Hamid is fully recovered.

At this very moment as I pen the final chapter of this book, he is alive and well. A bubbly, healthy, happy, young boy.

Just like any other.

Thankfully, the cancer has not recurred and we, the whole family, have complete faith in God that it shall never return.

Looking back now, I must say that this experience has been the most harrowing of my entire life. Sure, like anyone else, I have been through my own fair share of hardships in life but this was the most difficult thing I have to grapple with.

By far.

As a father, seeing my beloved son going through such an agonizing experience is gut wrenching, and I would not wish it on anyone.

The fear, the anxiety, the negative possibilities, the "what-ifs." It was all too much for me to bear and it is a miracle that I did not cave in to the pressure.

What I can say, without any shade of doubt, is that it made me a much stronger man than I have ever been. It did not kill me, neither did it any of my beloved ones. It just changed us by strengthening us. The Noor of today is a very different one from the Noor of just five years ago.

I am a much more resilient and self-assured man of faith. I came to see the hand of God and gained confidence that He truly does answer prayers, even in our darkest of moments.

So, while dealing with Neuroblastoma was indeed incredibly tough, there are, undoubtedly, some very important lessons I learned along the way that I think other people going through such a terrible experience such can benefit from.

One of the biggest lessons I learnt from this experience is **the importance of developing inner strength.** While it is important to have people to rely on, external strength can only take you far. Being able to stay calm and steadfast in the midst of any storm is truly a superpower that most people don't have but need to have. It will take you very far.

Dear friend, you have to learn how to tap into your inner strength. Trust me, facing the fact that your child has something as grievous as Neuroblastoma requires a level of strength you never imagined you had. It's like finding this hidden reserve of power inside you that helps you to push through even the toughest times.

One thing I have learned is that, if you want to truly develop inner strength, you have to cultivate self-awareness. It's the only way. I started my journey towards self-awareness by deliberately becoming more aware of my thoughts, fears, doubts, emotions, triggers, and reactions instead of sweeping them under the rug like I used to do.

In the midst of all the chaos surrounding me, I would find myself regularly having to take time away from everything and set aside personal time for myself for self-reflection, contemplation, meditation, and soul-searching. This self-awareness has formed my foundation for building inner strength.

And on top of needing inner strength, I also became cognizant of **the sheer importance of having a strong support**

system around me. While I had my immediate family and that was amazing, the support I got from my extended family, friends and community in Norway was priceless.

They were a major pillar of strength to us, without which this experience would have been a lot harder to overcome.

My friend, don't ever underestimate the power of support and community. When you're going through something as intense as Neuroblastoma, having a strong support system is absolutely crucial. The love, understanding, and encouragement from your family, friends, and medical team makes the world of difference during such a difficult journey.

Family ties also tend to get stronger during times of crises such as this. I came to learn how tough times have a way of bringing families closer together than ever before. You may think that you are close as a family, but tragedy will teach you that you can become even closer. There is always room for more intimacy and closer bonds. The thing is, you are forced to rely on each other for support, to share the heavy burdens, and to celebrate the victories as a team. Your bond becomes unbreakable, and it is a beautiful thing to witness.

So, what I would encourage you is to always keep your family closer than close. Don't allow small, petty disagreements to tear you apart from your family because, when all is said and done, they are all that you have, and this tragedy made this all the more clear to me.

I mean, don't get me wrong, I have always valued my family and we have always been very close, but seeing how my dear mother, siblings and relatives really came through for us made me appreciate them even more. Whenever I needed anything at any time, my mother or siblings would stop what they were doing to help me out.

My beloved wife Fardowsa and I did not have to bear it all on our own, and that was such a huge blessing. I now have no doubt that they will always have my back, no matter what, and I will likewise always have theirs.

There's no place like home, and family is home.

Another thing I came to truly appreciate is how important it is to celebrate all the small wins in life, regardless of how tiny or inconsequential it may seem to us at that moment. Sometimes, when we are going through mountains, we want to see big miracles happen at once, so much so that we are invisible to the small hills that are being levelled for us. We want to see the slaying of a monster, but don't recognize when the ant has been subdued.

No matter how tiny the victory may seem, remember that it's important to celebrate every milestone, be it big or small. Those little accomplishments are very crucial because they give you the much-needed hope that keeps you going when things feel tough. And they give the strength to accomplish the big victory. So embrace them!

I remember how I would always be so over the moon whenever Hamid would have a small win. Whenever he got through one treatment regimen successfully, whenever he would gain some strength, and when he started to eat again. All those moments were beautiful. They may have seemed small at the time but they were incremental and monumental in my eyes considering just how grave Neuroblastoma is.

Every small win was a big win to me!

In that same breath, I also learned just **how crucial it is to live in the moment.** Dealing with a serious illness like this, especially when it is your child who is affected, really teaches you to appreciate the here and now. Life is a gift and tomorrow is never promised. You start cherishing every single day and every single step, and finding joy in even the simplest of moments.

Time with your child and loved ones becomes so precious, you know?

I started to cherish every moment with Hamid, Ammaar, and my whole family. Every laugh, every conversation, every fun time I get to share with them is now more valuable than it ever was before. I love spending time with them and I try my best to be present with them, paying attention to the small joys and pleasures that we get to share. Nowadays, even when I find myself very busy, I try to make a conscious effort to pause and smell the coffee, so to speak.

Life is too short to not cherish each and every moment.

Take care of yourself, too. This became ever more clear to me when dealing with this disease. When you're grappling with something serious like Neuroblastoma, it's easy to put your own wellbeing on the backburner. It is so easy to become engulfed in the everyday humdrum of going for treatment after treatment that you forget to practice self-care but, trust me, self-care is even more important when going through trials and tribulations.

You will be of no use to the ones who need you the most when you are not 100% well yourself. If I had been sick, I would have been in no condition to take care of him. So, always remember that it's important to prioritize your own health and that of your family even when you are taking care of a sick person.

Focus on eating well, getting some exercise, spending quality time together, and finding ways to reduce stress.

It'll make a world of difference even in terms of how you show up for your loved ones, I promise you.

You likewise need to develop a fresh perspective on life and be grateful.

It is often said that "gratitude attracts blessings," and I observed this in my own life. The more grateful I was, the better Hamid seemed to become.

Dealing with a serious illness really has a way of shifting your attitude and your priorities. While work used to be the most important thing to me, overnight that changed and family then became the most important thing in my life. Suddenly, you start appreciating the little things in life and finding happiness in everyday moments. And let me tell you, feeling grateful for the milestones you achieve and the support you receive is a game-changer.

But this shift in perspective can only happen if you allow yourself to see things differently. Some people are so stubborn, but you can't afford to be that way in the face of adversity. You need to grow emotionally. Emotional growth is such a vital aspect of developing as a mature adult, and going through an experience like this can really change you emotionally. It opens your heart, deepens your empathy, and reminds you just how fragile life can be.

As men, we have been taught by society to be 'strong' and never show our emotions. But this is not healthy. And it certainly is not strength. Real strength comes when we are able to confront our emotions head on, with no fear and apology. Emotional intelligence is very necessary for both men and women.

Nowadays, instead of hiding my emotions and downplaying them, I have learnt how to feel my emotions fully and even be more vulnerable and emotionally available to my loved ones.

This is the only way to cope with hard times in a healthy manner.

The more emotionally available you are to other people, the more they become emotionally open to you and that allows all of you come together and face any adversity as a unit. If you, however, have your guard up, other people will not feel free with you and this prevents unity when dealing with a tragic event like a serious illness. In fact, holding in your emotions or hiding them from others will not make you be free to explore and try better options.

My experience with Hamid's illness taught me **the importance of cultivating emotional intelligence** and being emotionally open. Before his Neuroblastoma diagnosis, I did not have a strong bond with Hamid due to the geographical distance between us so we had not had the opportunity to bond emotionally.

Being together in Norway was the first time we had gotten the chance to truly connect, and that's when our emotional bond started to develop. I truly got to know my son, and he got to know me intimately as a father, and as we speak, we have a great father-son relationship.

Had it not been for this otherwise negative ordeal, we probably would not be as close as we are today. So, while it was a terrifying experience, it unwittingly helped us to grow close emotionally.

I additionally grew in knowledge and the experience overall taught me how important knowledge is. Ignorance is never a good thing especially when dealing with a unique disease like Neuroblastoma. It gives you so much peace of mind when you understand what kind of monster you are grappling with. Neuroblastoma forced me to do a lot of research on the disease. I spent countless hours on the Internet learning everything I could get my hands on about the disease, so much so that I can confidently describe myself as an expert on Neuroblastoma, my lack of medical credentials notwithstanding.

My friend, it is so important that you become a 'learning machine.' Trust me, educating yourself about a disease like

Neuroblastoma, the treatment options, and the available resources can be the difference between life and death. Literally. While it is important to trust your doctors, you must also educate yourself to make sure that you or your loved one gets the best treatment possible. The more you know, the better equipped you'll be to make informed decisions.

One interesting thing this experience taught me is that **children are stronger than you think.** Sometimes, as adults, we tend to underestimate the inner strength that children possess, but this experience taught me just how strong and resilient children can be.

It took this experience for me to see my son through new eyes; seeing him pull through every treatment, even the most brutal ones like chemotherapy, with a smile on his face, was truly mind-blowing and awe-inspiring. His strength gave me strength, ironically, and I am grateful that he was brave and resilient enough to face this disease gracefully because he gave me more strength and encouragement than he knew.

And finally, the most important message I must leave with you is: **Never lose hope, stay strong, and never, ever give up.** As long as you have breath inside of you, there is always a fighting chance so don't give in to your problems. **And always take time to pray to God; you are closer to God than you think,** and He is closer to you than you can ever imagine. As the Holy Quran says, *"I am truly near. I respond to one's prayer when they call upon Me. So let them respond 'with obedience' to Me and believe in Me, perhaps they will be guided 'to the Right Way"* (Quran. 2:186).

Well friend, there you have it—some real talk from someone who's been there, done that, and has the t-shirt to prove it. We overcame a harrowing experience; from learning that my son had cancer to coming out of it on the other side with a cancer-free victory. If we could do it, you too can.

I sincerely hope these lessons help you and others facing Neuroblastoma or any other disease, especially those with gravely ill children. If, through this book, I can manage to encourage even one person out there, then this scary experience will have been worth it. And my triumph over it will be our victory over any dark happening; be it of our own making or just a strange happenstance.

If you remember nothing else, remember this: that regardless of what the prognosis is, there is always hope. Stay strong and keep fighting, my friend. Educate yourself, seek support, and fight for your child's health. No matter what. Remember to savour the present, find joy in the small victories, and take time to take care of yourself, even in the midst of chaos. Be strong!

All in all, there is always the chance of a bright and beautiful rainbow at the end of every storm. All you have to do is believe.

Bibliography

American Cancer Society. Treatment of neuroblastoma. https://www.cancer.org/cancer/types/neuroblastoma/treating/by-risk-group.html#:~:text=Children%20at%20low%20risk%20usually,go%20away%20on%20their%20own (Accessed on 1st August 2023).

Ianadoctors.com. Medical marijuana and neuroblastoma. http://marijuanadoctors.com/conditions/neuroblastoma. (Accessed on 1st August 2023).

Michael Nel. https://radiopaedia.org/cases/93906/studies/112434?lang=us(Accessed on 1st August 2023).

Pasqualin, C. High Risk Neuroblastoma: Standard Clinical Practice Recommendations. Goustave Roussy Cancer Campus. https://siope.eu/media/documents/escp-webinar-22sept-slides.pdf. An espcp-webinar. (Accessed on 1st August 2023).

PET CT Scan - Get Lost, Purpose, Side Effect & Power Benefits. https://bookmerilab.com/tests/ct-scan/pet-ct-scan/. (Accessed on 1st August 2023).

Servaes, S. E., Hoffer, F. A., Smith, E. A., & Khanna, G. (2019). Imaging of Wilms tumor: An update. Pediatric Radiology, 49, 1441-1452

Acknowledgements

First and foremost, I would like to express my heartfelt gratitude to God and to all the individuals who have made this book possible. Without their unwavering support, encouragement, and contributions, this project would not have come to fruition.

I would also like to extend my deepest appreciation to my incredible son Hamid, the inspiration behind this book. Your resilience, bravery, and unwavering spirit in the face of Neuroblastoma have touched my heart and taught me profound lessons about life and love. You are my hero, and I am forever grateful for the strength and patience you have shown.

I would further like to extend grateful thanks to my mother who was with me throughout this ordeal, accompanying me from Norway to Kenya and back, and just being a great teacher in life during our many hospital stays.

I would also like to acknowledge my dear wife Fardowsa who has been my rock throughout this experience, and whose love and strength has been a constant source of strength. I know how hard this was for you, and I appreciate everything you did for Hamid and our entire family. We gave each other strength throughout this heart-wrenching ordeal and I would never have made it without you.

My siblings, relatives, neighbours and friends, all of who stood by us during this period– I am grateful to you all. Your help was tremendous, and I will never forget all the support you gave to my family and I materially, physically, emotionally, and through your consistent prayers. Your unwavering love, understanding, and support have been our rock during the darkest times. Your presence, kind words, and gestures of comfort have meant the world to us, and we couldn't have made it without you. Thank you for standing by us through the ups and downs of this challenging journey.

To the medical professionals who have been an integral part of our journey, your expertise, dedication, and compassionate care have made a tremendous difference in our lives and saved my son's life. Your tireless efforts to provide the best possible treatment and support have been invaluable, and we are eternally grateful for your commitment to helping children like my son. I would like to specially thank Dr. Ellen Ruud for quality-assuring the medical information in the chapter in question (Chapter 4).

I would also like to thank Dr. Sh. Ali Mohamed Salah and his friends such as Sh. Abdirashid, Sh. Ali Suufi and many others who prayed for my boy during the trying times when he was in intensive care unit and even afterwards.

I would also like to express my gratitude to the Royal Norwegian Embassy in Nairobi for helping us process our travelling documents in time as well as the organization Kreftforeningen for their support when we needed them.

Lastly, I would like to extend my appreciation to the readers of this book. Your interest in our story and your willingness to learn and empathize with the experiences of families affected by cancer is deeply meaningful. It is my hope that this book will provide comfort, inspiration, and a sense of solidarity to those facing similar challenges. In closing, this book is a tribute to all those affected by cancer and any other serious illness, especially their children, a testament to the power of resilience, and a reminder that love and hope can carry us through even the darkest of times.

Printed in Great Britain
by Amazon